FOOTBALL
maths

BLUE STRIP

DON SHAW & JOHN SHIELS

You are the manager

_____

Your team name

_____

Colour in your kit

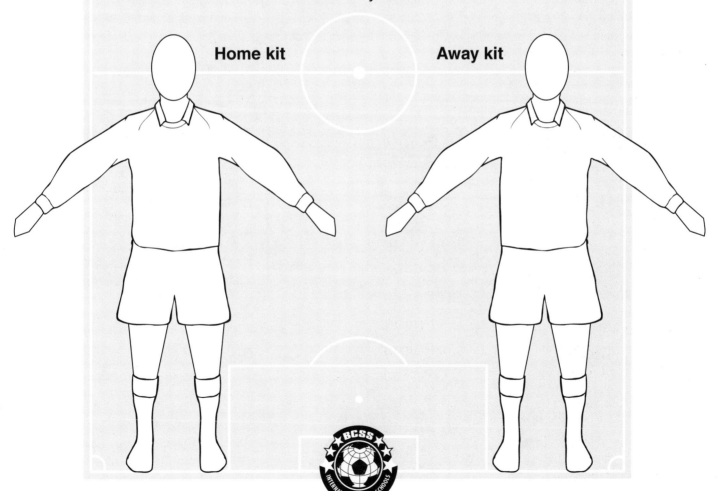

Home kit

Away kit

OXFORD UNIVERSITY PRESS

How to use this book

The purpose of this series of fill-in workbooks is to give practice in Key Stage 2 Maths in a motivating context.

The contents list shows which topic of maths is covered on each page, which maths skill this comes under, and at what level. This will give you some indication of how your child might perform in the National Tests.

First of all, your child should decide on their team name, write it in on the title page, and colour their kit in home and away colours. On each page they can decide on a different opponent, and fill in their own team in the white box and the opposing team in the tinted box. The away games are always slightly harder than the home games. The cup featured is a Global team competition and the teams chosen should reflect this.

There are three kinds of page, keyed in the top corner:

    League games, which cover exercises in number and data.

    Global Cup games, which are all on shape and measures.

    Training sessions, which are just games for practice, and don't involve scoring.

To check your child's answers after each page, turn to the referee's decisions on page 30. Fill in your goals down the right-hand side of each page and your final score at the foot of the page. Then complete the grids below: for each league game you win, fill in 3 points, starting from the bottom of the table; for a draw, fill in just 1 point. For each cup game you win, fill in a box, starting from the bottom. If you draw 0–0, stage a replay.

 League

Champions		48 Points
Runners-up		45 Points
European place		42 Points
European place		39 Points
		36 Points
		33 Points
		30 Points
Mid		27 Points
		24 Points
Table		21 Points
		18 Points
		15 Points
		12 Points
Relegated		9 Points
Relegated		6 Points
Relegated		3 Points

 Global Cup

	Final
	Semi-final
	Quarter-final
	3rd Round
	2nd Round
	1st Round

⚽ ⚽ ⚽ CONTENTS ⚽ ⚽ ⚽

Fill in your team names

	V	

A difficult first game. You'll do well to take anything from this fixture!

SOUVENIR SHOP

Hats £7.20

Badges £1.60

Key-ring £2.30

Poster £3.75

Tee-shirt £6.10

Mini kit £5

Videos £9

Sweat-shirts £32

Activity book £4.20

Scarf £5.80

Balls £15.60

Track-suit tops £18.70

Jog bottoms £19.95

1 How much change will you get from £10 if you buy the following items:

Hat

Activity book

Scarf

| change _____ | change _____ | change _____ |

goal

2 John buys one item and receives £8.40 change from £10.

What did he buy? _____

goal

3 Pete buys 2 items for £7.40. What did he buy? _____

goal

FINAL SCORE

	2	V		

4

Fill in your team names

	V	

Don't be put off by their big money additions, it's goals that count!

1 How much change will these people receive from £20?

Video £9.00	Video _____	Tee-shirt _____
Mini kit 5.00	Key-ring _____	Badge _____
Total cost 14.00	Total cost _____	Total cost _____
Change £6.00	Change _____	Change _____

Activity book _____	Poster _____	Hat _____
Poster _____	Badge _____	Tee-shirt _____
Total cost _____	Total cost _____	Badge _____
Change _____	Change _____	Total cost _____
		Change _____

goal

2 How much change will these people receive from £50?

Sweat-shirt _____	Video _____	Key-ring _____
Mini kit _____	Activity book _____	Badge _____
Total cost _____	Total cost _____	Total cost _____
Change _____	Change _____	Change _____

Track-suit top _____	Jog bottoms _____	Sweat-shirt _____
Ball _____	Hat _____	Badge _____
Total cost _____	Total cost _____	Poster _____
Change _____	Change _____	Total cost _____
		Change _____

goal

FINAL SCORE

	V		1

Fill in your team names

	V	

7-a-side tournament

Their defence is at sixes and sevens.
You should get lots of chances!

1

1 team has 1 set of 7 players:	1 × 7 = 7
2 teams have 2 sets of 7 players:	2 × 7 = ___
3 teams have 3 sets of 7 players:	3 × ___ = ___
4 teams have ___ sets of ___ players:	___ × ___ = ___
5 teams have ___ sets of ___ players:	___ × ___ = ___
6 teams have ___ sets of ___ players:	___ × ___ = ___
7 teams have ___ sets of ___ players:	___ × ___ = ___
8 teams have ___ sets of ___ players:	___ × ___ = ___
9 teams have ___ sets of ___ players:	___ × ___ = ___
10 teams have ___ sets of ___ players:	___ × ___ = ___

goal

2

There are 8 seats in each row.

1 row of 8 seats:	1 × 8 = 8
2 rows of 8 seats:	2 × 8 = ___
3 rows of 8 seats:	3 × ___ = ___
4 rows of 8 seats:	___ × ___ = ___
5 rows of ___ seats:	___ × ___ = ___
6 rows of ___ seats:	___ × ___ = ___
7 rows of ___ seats:	___ × ___ = ___
8 rows of ___ seats:	___ × ___ = ___
9 rows of ___ seats:	___ × ___ = ___
10 rows of ___ seats:	___ × ___ = ___

Directors' Box

goal

FINAL SCORE

	1	V		

6

Fill in your team names

[ ] V [ ]

The number of times your centre forward has been one on one with their keeper!

Each box contains 9 drinks.

1

1 box of 9 drinks: 1 × 9 = 9

2 boxes of 9 drinks: 2 × 9 = ___

3 boxes of 9 drinks: 3 × ___ = ___

4 boxes of 9 drinks: ___ × ___ = ___

5 boxes of ___ drinks: ___ × ___ = ___

6 boxes of ___ drinks: ___ × ___ = ___

7 boxes of ___ drinks: ___ × ___ = ___

8 boxes of ___ drinks: ___ × ___ = ___

9 boxes of ___ drinks: ___ × ___ = ___

10 boxes of ___ drinks: ___ × ___ = ___

goal

goal

2

Starting at 9, count in 9s up to 90.

9 → 18 → [ ] → [ ] → [ ] → [ ] → [ ] → [ ] → [ ] → 90

FINAL SCORE

[ ] V [ ] 1

7

[   ] V [   ]

Should be a high scoring game!

1 Fill in the empty boxes, following the number patterns.

7 → 14 → 21 → [ ] → [ ] → 42 → [ ] → [ ] → 63 → 70

8 → 16 → [ ] → 32 → [ ] → [ ] → [ ] → [ ] → [ ] → 80

9 → 18 → [ ] → [ ] → 45 → [ ] → [ ] → [ ] → [ ] → 90

goal

2 Now use these three number patterns to find three different routes to goal. Start at the halfway line with 7, 8, 9 and keep adding the same number to each.

The routes may cross, and you can use the same circle on different routes.

Colour in your three routes.

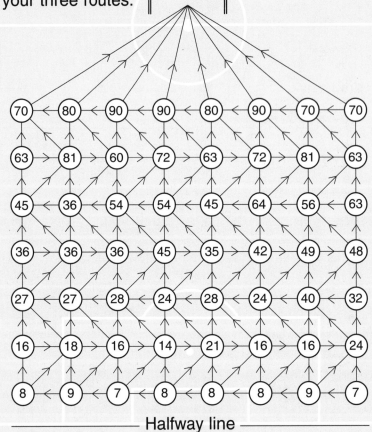

Halfway line

goals

FINAL SCORE

[   ] **3** V [   ]

	V	

One goal might decide it – make a point of getting your efforts on target!

Daily Globe

Sheffield sign Todd for £2.3m and May for £4.2m.

Daily Moon

Bolton sign Jones for £4.7m and Li for £3.2m.

Daily News

Villa sign Mills for £2.8m and Green for £3.5m.

Daily Sport

West Ham sign Day for £5.6m and Jones for £3.7m.

Evening News

Leeds sign Cope for £4.5m and Henry for £9.7m.

Evening Star

Chelsea sign Gray for £8.4m and Webb for £9.9m.

Daily Post

Newcastle sign 2 strikers for £12.5m and £5.8m.

1 Work out how much each team has spent.

Sheffield £_____
£_____
£_____

Villa £_____
£_____
£_____

Leeds £_____
£_____
£_____

Bolton £_____
£_____
£_____

West Ham £_____
£_____
£_____

Chelsea £_____
£_____
£_____

Newcastle £_____
£_____
£_____

goal

FINAL SCORE

	V	0

LEAGUE

[   ] **V** [   ]

You don't lose many away games. Don't spoil your record.

March					
Mon.		5	12	19	26
Tues.		6	13	20	27
Wed.		7	14	21	28
Thur.	1	8	15	22	29
Fri.	2	9	16	23	30
Sat.	3	10	17	24	31
Sun.	4	11	18	25	

Liverpool fixtures		
March	3 ...	Newcastle
	7 ...	Leeds
	10 ...	Blackburn
	14 ...	West Ham
	18 ...	Chelsea
	26 ...	Wimbledon
	31 ...	Tottenham
April	4 ...	Coventry

1 a) Which team do Liverpool play on 10 March? _____

b) Which team do Liverpool play on 26 March? _____

2 a) What day of the week is 1 March? _____

b) What day of the week is 5 March? _____

3 a) On what day of the week do Liverpool play Leeds? _____

b) On what day of the week do Liverpool play Chelsea? _____

c) On what day of the week do Liverpool play Tottenham? _____

d) On what day of the week do Liverpool play Coventry? _____

4 a) What will be the date of the first Saturday in April? _____

b) If February had 28 days what was the date of the last Saturday
   in February? _____

FINAL SCORE

[   ] **3** **V** [   ]

Fill in your team names

	V	

FIRST ROUND

Even if you need extra time, I'm sure you can finish them off!

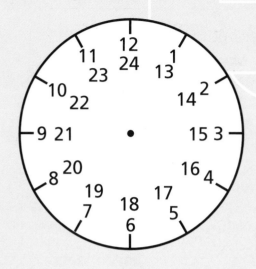

These World Cup Qualifiers are all taking place around the world on the same day.

The kick-off times have all been written down as 24-hour clock times.

Write them as 12-hour clock times using a.m. or p.m.

U.S.A. v Chile	**Denmark v Germany**	**Australia v New Zealand**
Los Angeles 0230	Copenhagen 1500	Sydney 0800
2.30 a.m.	3.00 p.m.	

goal

Japan v Pakistan	**China v India**	**Sweden v Holland**
Tokyo 1030	Beijing 1115	Stockholm 1300

goal

Iraq v Saudi Arabia	**Finland v Greece**	**Egypt v Malta**
Baghdad 1630	Helsinki 1645	Cairo 1740

goal

Iceland v Italy	**Mexico v Peru**	**Argentina v Brazil**
Rejkavik 1920	Mexico City 2250	Buenos Aires 2345

goal

FINAL SCORE

	V		0

11

V

Take the direct route to goal before they do!

Sue keeps a record of how long it takes her to travel to matches.

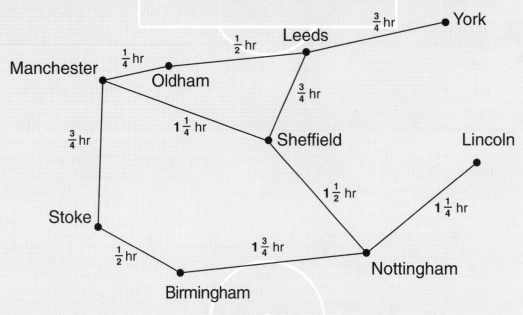

Example

Sue wants to watch her team Oldham play at York.

2 quarters + 3 quarters

It will take Sue $1\frac{1}{4}$ hours to travel from Oldham to York.

Using the map opposite, work out how long these journeys will take.

1 Manchester to Leeds   Total time _____

Manchester to Nottingham   Total time _____

goal

2 Lincoln to Birmingham   Total time _____

Birmingham to Sheffield   Total time _____

goal

3 Stoke to Oldham   Total time _____

Birmingham to Manchester   Total time _____

goal

4 Leeds to Nottingham   Total time _____

Sheffield to York   Total time _____

goal

FINAL SCORE

| | | v | | 3 |

Fill in your team names

[grey box]	V	[ ]

Concentrate on linking defence with attack to plot an upset!

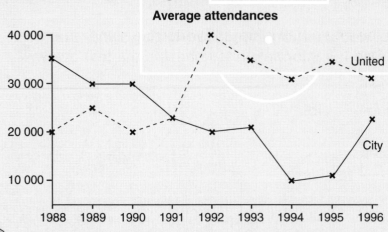

Average attendances

1 Complete this chart showing both teams' attendances.

Year	United	City
1988	20 000	
1989		
1990		
1992		

goal

2

a) Write down United's average attendance in 1994. _____

b) Write down City's average attendance in 1995. _____

c) Write down United's average attendance in 1996. _____

d) In which year did the 2 teams have the same average attendance?

_____

e) In which year did City have their lowest average attendance?

_____

f) In which year did United have their highest average attendance?

_____

goal

FINAL SCORE

[grey box]	**1**	V	[ ]

They've had an up and down season. You can move up after this one!

This graph shows how the noise builds up at Everton's ground on one particular match night. Use the information to complete the text below.

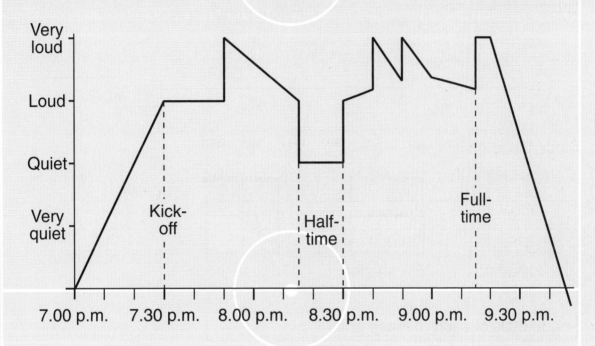

The noise builds up to loud for the kick-off at _____ . The noise stays

loud until Everton score their first goal at _____ when it becomes

_____ . The whistle blows for half-time at _____ and the noise

level drops to _____ . The second half begins at _____ with the

noise level at _____ . Everton score 2 goals in the second half at

_____ and _____ . The final whistle blows at _____ and the noise

level increases to _____ for about _____ . The noise then takes

about _____ to die down as everybody makes their way home.

goal

FINAL SCORE

V

0

CUP

V

SECOND ROUND

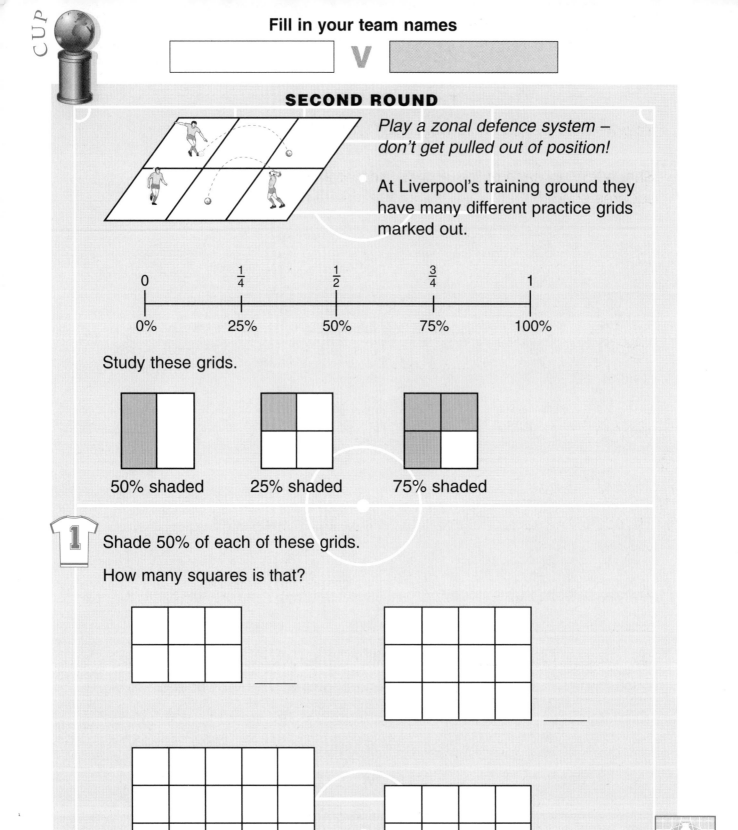

Play a zonal defence system – don't get pulled out of position!

At Liverpool's training ground they have many different practice grids marked out.

0   $\frac{1}{4}$ $\frac{1}{2}$ $\frac{3}{4}$ 1

0%   25%   50%   75%   100%

Study these grids.

50% shaded   25% shaded   75% shaded

Shade 50% of each of these grids.

How many squares is that?

FINAL SCORE

V   0

[ ] V [ ]

CUP

THIRD ROUND

Your midfield players must work hard up and back from box to box!

1 Shade 25% of each of these grids, and write the number of squares shaded.

_____

_____

_____

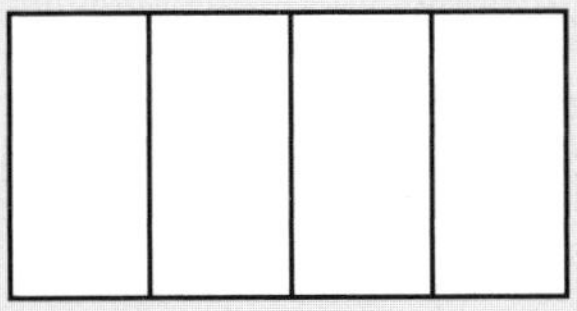

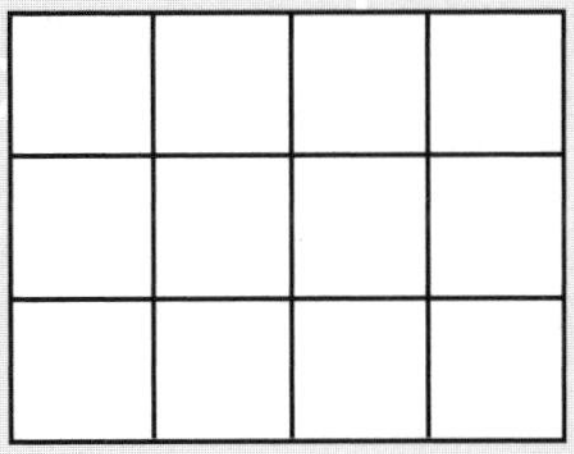

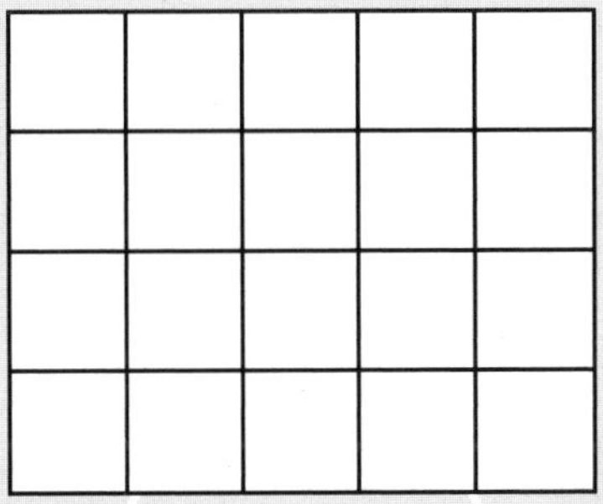

2 Shade 75% of each of these grids, and write the number of squares shaded.

_____

_____

goal

goal

_____

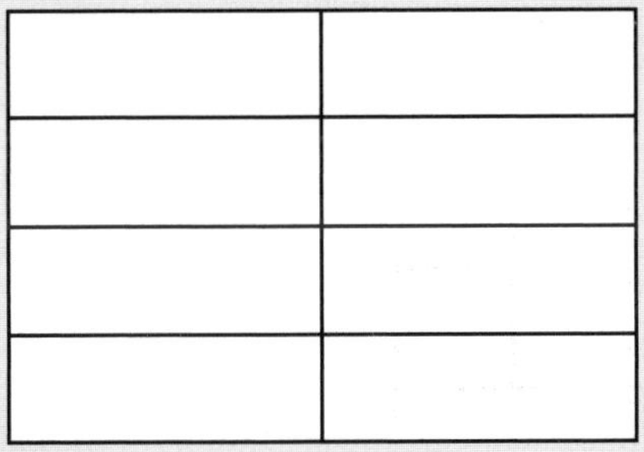

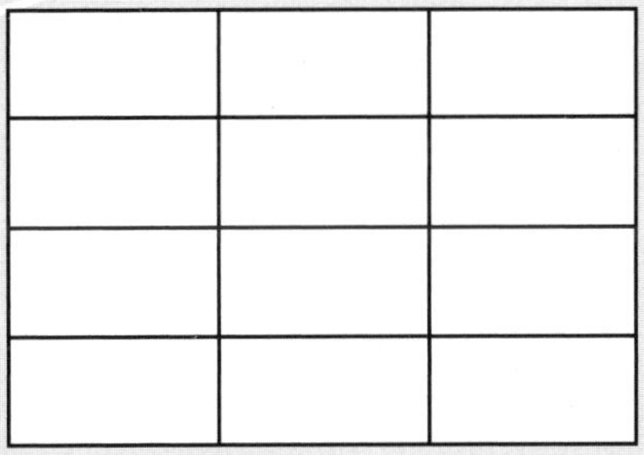

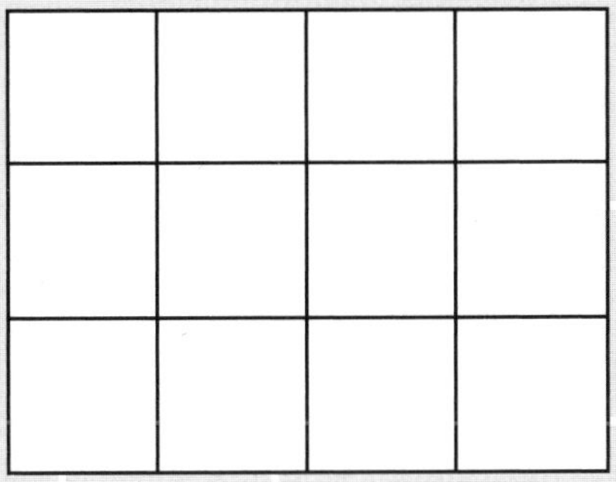

FINAL SCORE

[ ] V [ ] **0**

17

Work out the sums and colour in the picture.

18	Brown
24	Orange
36	Red
40	Yellow
48	Green
56	Pink
60	Light blue
63	Black

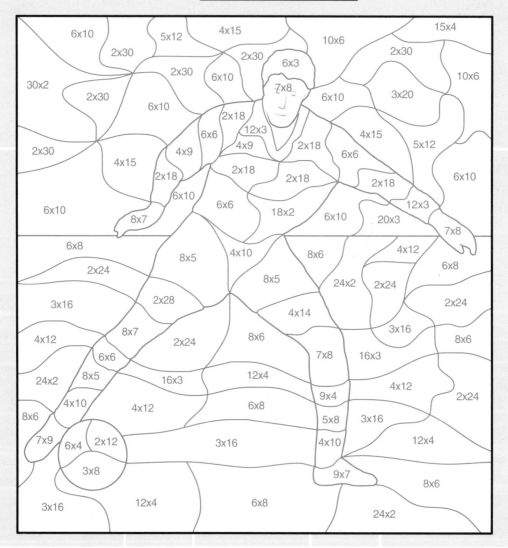

	V	

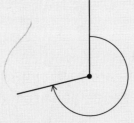

QUARTER-FINAL

Your attackers can spin and turn their markers, and be in on goal!

A right angle is a $\frac{1}{4}$ turn.

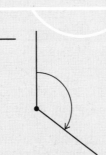

A straight line is a $\frac{1}{2}$ turn.

An acute angle is smaller than a $\frac{1}{4}$ turn.

An obtuse angle is bigger than a $\frac{1}{4}$ turn but smaller than a $\frac{1}{2}$ turn.

A reflex angle is bigger than a $\frac{1}{2}$ turn.

A passes to B who turns and passes to C.

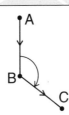

B has turned through an obtuse angle.

1 State what type of angles these people have turned through to make the passes.

A

B

C

D

goal

_____   _____   _____   _____

2

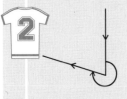

goal

_____   _____   _____   _____

FINAL SCORE

	V		**0**

Fill in your team names

	V	

Their defensive problems are multiplying – keep up the pressure!

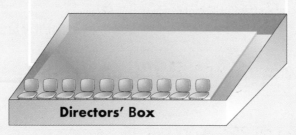

Directors' Box

They are putting new seats in the Directors' Box. The first row of 10 seats has been put in. How many rows will make a total of 40 seats?

$$\boxed{} \times 10 = 40$$

There will be 4 rows in this box.

The first row of seats has been put into these boxes. Work out how many rows are needed to fill them.

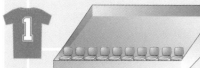

Seats 60

$10 \times \underline{\hspace{1cm}} = 60$

Seats 24

$6 \times \underline{\hspace{1cm}} = 24$

Seats 36

$9 \times \underline{\hspace{1cm}} = 36$

goal

Seats 48

$8 \times \underline{\hspace{1cm}} = 48$

Seats 40

$8 \times \underline{\hspace{1cm}} = 40$

Seats 56

$7 \times \underline{\hspace{1cm}} = 56$

goal

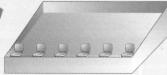

Seats 36

$6 \times \underline{\hspace{1cm}} = 36$

Seats 72

$8 \times \underline{\hspace{1cm}} = 72$

Seats 45

$9 \times \underline{\hspace{1cm}} = 45$

goal

FINAL SCORE

		V		2

Fill in your team names

	V	

Play a percentage game – wait for their mistakes and make them pay the price!

SOUVENIR SHOP

End of Season Sale: 25% off all prices

If all items are reduced by 25% work out the sale prices.

Top £24

Bottoms £20

Shorts £12

goal

Socks £8

Hat £6

Ball £18

goal

Keeper's top £25

Keeper's gloves £12.80

Book £7.20

goal

FINAL SCORE

	2	V	

	V	

SEMI-FINAL

You're better in all areas of your game – even penalty taking! Go for it!

The groundsman is cutting the grass.

The shaded part shows how much grass has been cut.

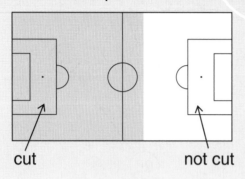

cut   not cut

How much of the pitch has he cut?

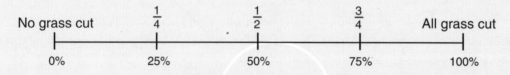

He has cut just over half of the grass.

We can estimate that he has cut about 60% of the grass.

1 Estimate the percentage of grass cut on these pitches. The shaded section shows the grass cut.

about ____ % cut   about ____ % cut   about ____ % cut

about ____ % cut   about ____ % cut   about ____ % cut

goals

FINAL SCORE

	V		0

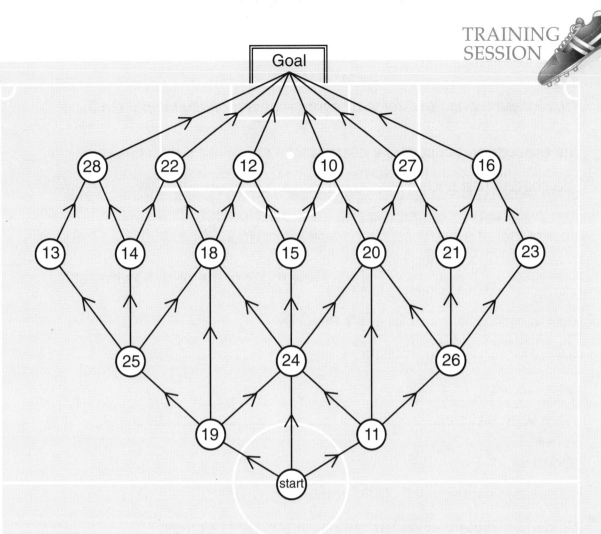

The game is for 2 players. The game lasts 10 minutes.

One player is the attacker and the other is the defender. Players change round after 5 minutes.

The attacker moves the counter one place in any direction.

The defender rolls the dice.

If the number on the dice divides exactly into the number that the counter is on, then the attacker has been tackled and the counter is moved back one place. If the number on the dice does not divide exactly into the number that the counter is on, then the counter does not move.

The attacker moves the counter one place and the process is repeated.

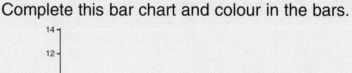

This will be a good test to chart your progress this season!

1 Steve keeps a record of the attendances at Athletic's matches during a season. He records the information by size of attendance, and by how often there was that size of attendance. The first line means that at 5 matches there were attendances from 0 up to 5000. The second line means that at 9 matches there were attendances from 5001 to 10 000.

Attendance	Frequency
0–5000	5
5001–10 000	9
10 001–15 000	13
15 001–20 000	10
20 001–25 000	3

Complete this bar chart and colour in the bars.

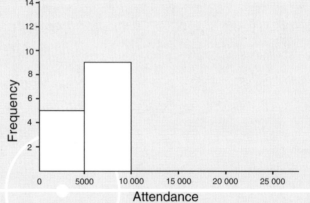

What was the most frequent size of attendance?

2 Sandy keeps a record during a season of the times in the match when Rovers score their goals. Complete the tally chart, then draw a bar chart to show the times when goals are scored.

Time	Tally	Frequency
0–15	IIII	4
16–30	IIII II	7
31–45	IIII IIII III	
46–60	III	
61–75	IIII IIII	
76–90	IIII IIII IIII I	

When was the most frequent time for scoring goals?

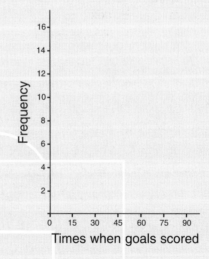

goal

FINAL SCORE

1

	V	

You're strong through the centre of the team, and head and shoulders above the opposition!

The *median* value of a group of numbers is the middle number after the numbers have been placed in order.

Example

Find the median height of these players:

180 cm   174 cm   150 cm   193 cm   161 cm

To find the median value we must place them in order of size.

150 cm   161 cm   174 cm   180 cm   193 cm

↑

The median value is 174 cm.

1 For each group place the values in order and find the median value.

Players' ages

Li	Peters	Eyre
27	23	19
Henry	Bell	Higson
29	17	34
	Conen	
	26	

Median =

Goals scored

Smith	Rogers	Bowdler
29	23	5
Morris	Parr	
21	16	

Median =

Team points

Leeds	Liverpool	City	
46	75	54	
Chelsea	United	Derby	Rangers
68	83	42	61
Tottenham		West Ham	
38		49	

Median =

Games played

Day	Jones	Flynn	Lee
48	97	26	246
Webb	Moore	Todd	
195	347	163	

Median =

goals

FINAL SCORE

	V	
3		

25

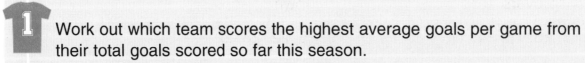

V

They are only an average side – you can win this one!

The *mean* value of a group of numbers is the *average* value, rather than the *middle* value.

To calculate the mean of a group of figures you add up all the figures and divide by the number of figures.

Example

What is the mean number of goals scored by each of these players, and whose mean is higher?

Treslove		Bowdler
26, 13, 20, 25	*or*	22, 20, 24
goals in last 4 seasons		goals in last 3 seasons

26 + 13 + 20 + 25 = 84   22 + 20 + 24 = 66

84 goals in 4 seasons   66 goals in 3 seasons

Mean = 84 ÷ 4 = 21   Mean = 66 ÷ 3 = 22

21 goals per season   22 goals per season

Bowdler is the better striker!

1 Work out which team scores the highest average goals per game from their total goals scored so far this season.

Liverpool	Tottenham	Newcastle
4, 2, 0, 0, 4, 3, 1, 4, 0	2, 3, 4, 5, 6, 4	1, 2, 2, 4, 3, 3, 5, 4
Total goals =	Total goals =	Total goals =
mean =	mean =	mean =

Highest mean _____

goal

2 City's manager wants to buy a striker.

He has to choose between 3 strikers.

He decides to buy the one with the highest mean goals per season.

Work out each player's mean goals per season:

Edwards

23, 17, 18, 24, 23

goals in 5 seasons

Matthews

26, 22, 24

goals in 3 seasons

Dean

30, 12, 26, 20

goals in 4 seasons

Total =

mean =

Total =

mean =

Total =

mean =

goal

Which player does he buy? _____

3 Here are the ages of all the players in two teams. Work out the mean age of each team.

Rovers

29, 18, 25, 18, 24, 17

22, 19, 21, 18, 20

Town

16, 19, 25, 22, 28, 22

20, 24, 22, 21, 23

Total age =

mean age =

Total age =

mean age =

goal

Which is the older team? _____

FINAL SCORE

| | | V | | 2 |

V

Their defence is all over the place, whereas you're going straight to the top!

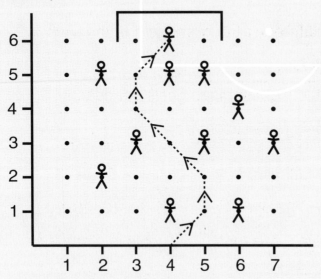

To score a goal a player has to find a route to goal that avoids the defenders.

The route shown on the diagram does not score a goal because the goalkeeper saves the shot.

Which of these players scores?

1

Player A   (1,1)–(1,2)–(1,3)–(2,4)–(3,5)–(3,6)

Player B   (3,1)–(3,2)–(2,3)–(2,4)–(2,5)

Player C   (6,0)–(7,1)–(6,2)–(6,3)–(5,4)–(6,5)–(5,6)   Ans: _____

2

Player D   (7,1)–(6,2)–(6,3)–(5,4)–(6,5)–(4,6)

Player E   (2,1)–(3,2)–(4,3)–(5,4)–(6,5)–(6,6)

Player F   (5,0)–(5,1)–(6,2)–(6,3)–(5,4)–(4,4)–(4,5)   Ans: _____

3

Player G   (3,1)–(3,2)–(2,3)–(2,4)–(3,4)–(4,4)–(5,5)

Player H   (7,1)–(6,2)–(5,2)–(4,3)–(5,4)–(6,5)–(5,6)

Player I   (1,3)–(1,4)–(2,4)–(3,4)–(4,4)–(3,5)–(4,6)   Ans: _____

FINAL SCORE

V

2

V

CUP FINAL

A last, final effort! The whole country will go crazy if you win!

During the summer the ground staff repair the worn parts of the pitch.

They mark out 11 areas to be reseeded.

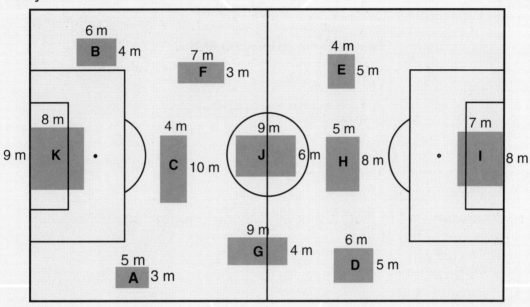

The area of Ⓐ is 3 × 5 = 15 square metres

The area of Ⓑ is 4 × 6 = _____ square metres

The area of Ⓒ is _____ = _____

The area of Ⓓ is _____ = _____

The area of Ⓔ is _____ = _____

The area of Ⓕ is _____ = _____

The area of Ⓖ is _____ = _____

The area of Ⓗ is _____ = _____

The area of Ⓘ is _____ = _____

The area of Ⓙ is _____ = _____

The area of Ⓚ is _____ = _____

FINAL SCORE

V

0

ANSWERS

The referee's decision is final!

▶ PAGE 4

One goal for each totally correct answer.

1 £2.80, £5.80, £4.20

2 Badge

3 Scarf and a badge

▶ PAGE 5

1

£ 9	£ 9	£ 6.10
£ 5	£ 2.30	£ 1.60
£14	£11.30	£ 7.70
£ 6	£ 8.70	£12.30
£ 4.20	£ 3.75	£ 7.20
£ 3.75	£ 1.60	£ 6.10
£ 7.95	£ 5.35	£ 1.60
£12.05	£14.65	£14.90
		£ 5.10

Four or more totally correct answers scores a goal.

2

£32	£ 9	£ 2.30
£ 5	£ 4.20	£ 1.60
£37	£13.20	£ 3.90
£13	£36.80	£46.10
£18.70	£19.95	£32
£15.60	£ 7.20	£ 1.60
£34.30	£27.15	£ 3.75
£15.70	£22.85	£37.35
		£12.65

Four or more totally correct answers scores a goal.

▶ PAGE 6

1
$2 \times 7 = \underline{14}$ $7 \times \underline{7} = \underline{49}$
$3 \times \underline{7} = \underline{21}$ $8 \times \underline{7} = \underline{56}$
$4 \times \underline{7} = \underline{28}$ $9 \times \underline{7} = \underline{63}$
$5 \times \underline{7} = \underline{35}$ $10 \times \underline{7} = \underline{70}$
$6 \times \underline{7} = \underline{42}$

Seven or more correct answers scores a goal.

2
$2 \times 8 = \underline{16}$ $7 \times 8 = \underline{56}$
$3 \times 8 = \underline{24}$ $8 \times \underline{8} = \underline{64}$
$4 \times \underline{8} = \underline{32}$ $9 \times \underline{8} = \underline{72}$
$5 \times \underline{8} = \underline{40}$ $10 \times \underline{8} = \underline{80}$
$6 \times \underline{8} = \underline{48}$

Seven or more correct answers scores a goal.

▶ PAGE 7

1
$2 \times 9 = \underline{18}$ $7 \times \underline{9} = \underline{63}$
$3 \times \underline{9} = \underline{27}$ $8 \times \underline{9} = \underline{72}$
$4 \times \underline{9} = \underline{36}$ $9 \times \underline{9} = \underline{81}$
$5 \times \underline{9} = \underline{45}$ $10 \times \underline{9} = \underline{90}$
$6 \times \underline{9} = \underline{54}$

Seven or more correct answers scores a goal.

2 27 → 36 → 45 → 54 → 63 → 72 → 81

Five or more correct answers scores a goal.

▶ PAGE 8

1 *Twelve or more correct answers scores a goal.*

7 → 14 → 21 → 28 → 35 → 42 → 49 → 56 → 63 → 70

8 → 16 → 24 → 32 → 40 → 48 → 56 → 64 → 72 → 80

9 → 18 → 27 → 36 → 45 → 54 → 63 → 72 → 81 → 90

2 *Each correct answer scores a goal.*

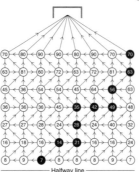

Counting in 7s

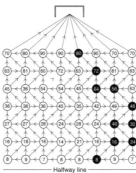

Counting in 8s

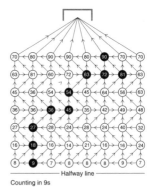

Counting in 9s

▶ PAGE 9

1

Team	Total amount spent (millions)
Sheffield	£2.3 + £4.2 = £6.5 m
Bolton	£4.7 + £3.2 = £7.9 m
Villa	£2.8 + £3.5 = £6.3 m
West Ham	£5.6 + £3.7 = £9.3 m
Leeds	£4.5 + £9.7 = £14.2 m
Chelsea	£8.4 + £9.9 = £18.3 m
Newcastle	£12.5 + £5.8 = £18.3 m

Five or more correct answers scores a goal.

▶ PAGE 10

1 Blackburn, Wimbledon

Both correct answers scores a goal.

2 Thursday, Monday

Both correct answers scores a goal.

3 Wednesday, Sunday, Saturday, Wednesday

Four correct answers scores a goal.

4 7 April, 24 February

Both correct answers scores a goal.

▶ PAGE 11

1 8.00 a.m.

2 10.30 a.m., 11.15 a.m., 1.00 p.m.

Three correct answers scores a goal.

3 4.30 p.m., 4.45 p.m., 5.40 p.m.

Three correct answers scores a goal.

4 7.20 p.m., 10.50 p.m., 11.45 p.m.

Three correct answers scores a goal.

▶ PAGES 12 and 13

1 $\frac{3}{4}$ hr, $2\frac{3}{4}$ hrs (or 3 hrs)

Both correct answers scores a goal.

2 3 hrs, $3\frac{1}{4}$ hrs (or $2\frac{1}{2}$ hrs)

Both correct answers scores a goal.

3 1 hr, $1\frac{1}{4}$ hrs

Both correct answers scores a goal.

4 $2\frac{1}{4}$ hrs, $1\frac{1}{2}$ hrs

Both correct answers scores a goal.

▶ PAGE 14

1

Year	United	City
1988	20 000	35 000
1989	25 000	30 000
1990	20 000	30 000
1992	40 000	20 000

Five or more correct answers scores a goal.

2 31 000, 12 000, 32 000,
1991, 1994, 1992

Four or more correct answers scores a goal.

▶ PAGE 15

1 7.30 p.m., 7.50 p.m., very loud,
8.15 p.m., quiet, 8.30 p.m., loud,
8.40 p.m., 8.50 p.m., 9.15 p.m.,
very loud, 5 mins, 25 mins

Ten or more correct answers scores a goal.

▶ PAGE 16

1

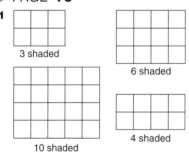

3 shaded

6 shaded

10 shaded

4 shaded

Three or more correct answers scores a goal.

▶ PAGE 17

1

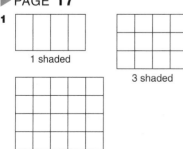

1 shaded

3 shaded

5 shaded

Three correct answers scores a goal.

2

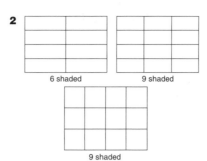

6 shaded

9 shaded

9 shaded

Three correct answers scores a goal.

▶ PAGE 19

1

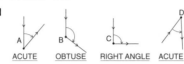

ACUTE   OBTUSE   RIGHT ANGLE   ACUTE

Three or more correct answers scores a goal.

2

REFLEX   ACUTE   OBTUSE   REFLEX

Three or more correct answers scores a goal.

▶ PAGE 20

1 Seats 60   Seats 24   Seats 36
$10 \times \underline{6} = 60$ $6 \times \underline{4} = 24$ $9 \times \underline{4} = 36$

Three correct answers scores a goal.

2 Seats 48   Seats 40   Seats 56
$8 \times \underline{6} = 48$ $8 \times \underline{5} = 40$ $7 \times \underline{8} = 56$

Three correct answers scores a goal.

3 Seats 36   Seats 72   Seats 45
$6 \times \underline{6} = 36$ $8 \times \underline{9} = 72$ $9 \times \underline{5} = 45$

Three correct answers scores a goal.

▶ PAGE 21

1 £18, £15, £9

Three correct answers scores a goal.

2 £6, £4.50, £13.50

Three correct answers scores a goal.

3 £18.75, £9.60, £5.40

Three correct answers scores a goal.

▶ PAGE 22

1 Actual areas, also allow areas in
brackets.
80% (70 to 90), 25% (15 to 35),
90% (85 to 95), 10% (5 to 15),
75% (65 to 85), 40% (35 to 45)

Each correct answer scores a goal.

▶ PAGE 24

1

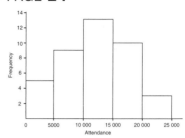

10 001 to 15 000 most frequent

Both correct answers scores a goal.

2

Time	Tally	Frequency
0–15	IIII	4
16–30	HHT II	7
31–45	HHT HHT III	13
46–60	III	3
61–75	HHT IIII	9
76–90	HHT HHT HHT I	16

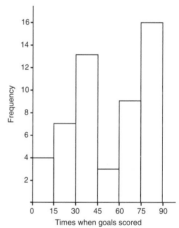

75 to 90 mins most frequent

All correct to score a goal.

▶ PAGE 25

1   21   26
163   54

Each correct answer scores a goal.

▶ PAGE 26

1 Liverpool   Total = 18   mean = 2
Tottenham   Total = 24   mean = 4
Newcastle   Total = 24   mean = 3

Tottenham has the highest mean

Final correct answer scores a goal.

2 Edwards   Total = 105   mean = 21
Matthews   Total = 72   mean = 24
Dean   Total = 88   mean = 22

He should buy Matthews

Final correct answer scores a goal.

3 Rovers   Total = 231   mean = 21
Town   Total = 242   mean = 22

Town is the older team

Final correct answer scores a goal.

1 A scores, B does not score, C scores

Two or more correct answers scores a goal.

2 D does not score, E does not score, F does not score

Two or more correct answers scores a goal.

3 G does not score, H scores, I does not score

Two or more correct answers scores a goal.

1 The area of Ⓑ is 4×6 = _24_ square metres

The area of Ⓒ is _4×10_ = _40 square metres_

The area of Ⓓ is _5×6_ = _30 square metres_

The area of Ⓔ is _4×5_ = _20 square metres_

The area of Ⓕ is _3×7_ = _21 square metres_

The area of Ⓖ is _4×9_ = _36 square metres_

The area of Ⓗ is _5×8_ = _40 square metres_

The area of Ⓘ is _7×8_ = _56 square metres_

The area of Ⓙ is _6×9_ = _54 square metres_

The area of Ⓚ is _8×9_ = _72 square metres_

Seven or more correct answers scores a goal.

Bobby Charlton Soccer Schools
'Learning through Football'

Special School courses are available at the Bobby Charlton Soccer School HQ in Manchester throughout the year, either residentially or non residential. All participants will be able to tackle the problems of Key Stage 2 Maths and English, as well as receive expert tuition putting them through their soccer paces. There will also be an opportunity to visit the great Manchester attractions of Manchester United FC and Granada Tours. For further details contact John Shiels at Bobby Charlton Sports School, Hopwood Hall, Rochdale Road, Middleton, Manchester, M24 6XH or Telephone: 0161 643 3113 Fax: 0161 643 1444.

Individual courses in Maths and football are available each Easter vacation.

Oxford University Press, Great Clarendon Street, Oxford OX2 6DP

Oxford New York
Athens Auckland Bangkok Bogota Bombay Buenos Aires
Calcutta Cape Town Dar es Salaam Delhi
Florence Hong Kong Istanbul Karachi
Kuala Lumpur Madras Madrid Melbourne
Mexico City Nairobi Paris Singapore
Taipei Tokyo Toronto Warsaw

and associated companies in
Berlin Ibadan

Oxford is a trade mark of Oxford University Press

© Oxford University Press 1998
First published 1998
Reprinted 1999

ISBN 019 838226 X

Typeset and designed by Oxford Designers & Illustrators, Oxford

Printed in Hong Kong